The children went to see Gran.
They were going to spend the night.

"We can have some fun!" said Gran.
"Well, be good," said Mum.

"I have a loft in the roof," said Gran.
"You can have it as a den."

They went up the steps.
The steps were too steep for Floppy.

"It's like a tent," said Biff.
"I can just stand up," said Chip.

Gran had some cans of paint.
"You can paint the loft pink, black and green," she said.

"There are some lumps in this one," said Chip.

They went back up to the loft.
They had to sand it down.

"That was hard," said Chip.
"Now we can start painting," said Biff.

"Let's paint this part green," said Biff.
"Hand me that paint pot," said Chip.

"I will paint this pink," said Kipper.

"I have some stickers and blankets for you," said Gran.

She put a lamp on the shelf.

One part of the loft had silver stars.
One part was pink and green.

"You can sleep in the loft tonight,"
said Gran.

"They had lots of fun," said Gran.
"But they did not sleep a wink!"